chris
cartoons
VOLUME ONE

AXOLOTL PUBLICATIONS

AXOLOTL PUBLICATIONS

This collection first published in 1989
by Axolotl Publications
3 Stormyhill Road, Portree, Isle of Skye IV51 9DZ

The individual cartoons first published by
the *West Highland Free Press* between 1979 and 1989

Copyright © Chris Tyler

Printed by West Highland Publishing Company Limited,
Industrial Estate, Broadford, Isle of Skye IV49 9AP

ISBN 0 9514685 0 2

It is now 10 years since Santa Claus appeared on the front page of the **Free Press** being breathalysed after colliding with a police car in Glen Varagill . . . my first cartoon, Christmas 1978.

You will probably notice the variety of size and style of cartoons in this book. This is largely due to the variety of places in which they were drawn — some were scribbled on a piece of scrap card in the foc'sle of a trawler, others in various pubs from the Pier Hotel to the "Puff Inn" on St Kilda. The really fancy ones were done in the comfort of the **Free Press** office, with ample supplies of drawing equipment — you can probably work out which ones were done where.

I have greatly enjoyed reading through back issues of the paper to assemble this book, and I hope that this selection of cartoons from the past 10 years will bring back memories for regular **Free Press** readers. And if your favourite cartoon is not here, fear not! It will probably be in volume two.

Of course, for those of you who have not come across my work before there is a simple solution — buy the **West Highland Free Press** every week!

For
Jenny, David, Andy,
little Chris
and Beatrice

"I don't care if you do have a ferry to catch, would you mind blowing into this bag, sir!"

chris

Christmas '78

"Well, it's not *my* idea of an unbiased poll!"

23.2.79

CIVIL SERVANTS THREATEN GUGHA HUNT

"Mind it's only the white ones we're going after!"

"No crofters or fishermen on the Entrepreneurial Commando Courses"

The HIDB have engaged an American company to seek out "high-flying entrepreneurs" with development ideas worthy of board investment. The man behind the Venture Founders scheme, a Mr Alexander LM Dingee, envisages "only the strongest" surviving his high-pressure weekend commando courses for the ideas men. One of the board's dafter notions, this scheme seems likely only to further alienate it from the people it is supposed to serve.

23.1.81

Last week, the *Free Press* reported on an HIDB-backed plan to manufacture "Japanese-style ornaments" in Harris. Cartoonist CHRIS comments above . . .

27.3.81

"And when we've pocketed this grant the NCC will pay us £200,000 not to go ahead!"

HIDB scheme to help make the rich richer

The Highlands and Islands Development Board this week unveiled a new scheme which will put more public cash into the coffers of already-wealthy landlords . . .

. . . The types of project the Board apparently have in mind include "setting up all-weather facilities, creating clay pigeon or fly casting centres, wildlife parks or converting disused farm buildings and letting them as craft workshops or to tradesmen". . .

4.3.88

HIDB in bid to promote "sporting" holidays

The Highlands and Islands Development Board are backing a scheme aimed at attracting tourists with a special interest in slaughtering deer for "sport".

The Board have given assistance to a Highland "field sport" (sic) agency which is producing a promotional tape to lure hunting, shooting and fishing enthusiasts to the area . . .

25.4.86

"Well, I guess it's one way to make the dole money go further!"

Tebbit's Law joined forces with the Army in the Highlands last week, with the introduction of an adventure training scheme aimed at temporarily alleviating the boredom and frustration of life on the dole for the country's teenagers.

The 300 attending the initial course, under the supervision of 80 hand-picked instructors, will climb, canoe and cavort in hills, glens and lochs throughout the Lochaber area in particular.

A four-day expedition to that area will teach them survival techniques, including how to live without food for long periods. During this spell, they will be taught how to survive on a diet of dandelions and mussels, as well as how to skin rabbits . . .

"It's just as well he didn't win the election — she'd probably have made him an archbishop!"

Following his dramatic defeat in Ross, Cromarty and Skye by the young SDP candidate Charles Kennedy in last week's General Election, Mr Hamish Gray has been elevated to the House of Lords and made a Minister of State with special responsibility for Highland affairs . . .

28.5.82

17.6.83

Reports that the Scottish Transport Group — which includes Caledonian MacBrayne and Highland Scottish Omnibuses — are high on the Government's privatisation list have led to widespread concern in the Highlands and Islands . . .

"Sorry, sir, unless you have the cash or are a member of BUPA . . ."

Just after gaining the contract for the search and rescue service based at Stornoway, it has come to light that Bristow Helicopters have presented proposals to the Ministry of Defence to privatise the whole SAR operation.

Bristows — who approached the MoD with their proposals in February — claim that if the service was handed over to civilian contractors a saving of 45 per cent could be made on the £53 million operation . . .

"I'll be back to sew you up when I've raised enough money
for the thread!"

"Of course, the Government insisted we had to accept the
lowest tender . . ."

Highland Health Board are considering contracting out replacement hip operations to private hospitals, in a bid to reduce the waiting list . . .

28.1.83

15.1.88

The first major demonstration of the inherent pitfalls of share ownership for small investors came this week with a record crash on stock markets around the world.

Share prices in nearly every company, and all of the Tory-privatised industries, took a deep plunge and BP share prices — the latest Government privatisation candidate — even fell well below their giveaway issue price.

October '87

The name game

That's it settled. Let nobody say that the Democrats — formerly the Social and Liberal Democrats, also known as the SLD, quite recently called the Alliance, and not that long ago the Liberals and the SDP — cannot make up their minds.

They are now quite firmly Democrats — that is unless they choose to call themselves Social and Liberal Democrats.

For the record (and to avoid confusion in his traditionally Liberal consituency of Ross, Cromarty and Skye) Charles Kennedy MP voted to be a Democrat. However, that must be qualifed by the fact that he can describe himself as a Scottish Democrat, or, if he so chooses, a Scottish Social and Liberal Democrat, or Liberal Democrat, or alternatively, just plain Democrat.

30.9.88

"I can remember when they just used to kiss babies!"

. . .Two separate SLD correspondences to an address in Sleat, Skye, recently yielded a total of six ballot papers (for miscellaneous elections), 13 attached electioneering leaflets (from miscellaneous candidates), five news leaflets, two return envelopes and a registration form for the new party.

Such a bin-full of bumph might be enough to keep the most committed SLD supporter chewing for the entire summer, but it proved just too much for the two-and-a-half-year-old infant it was addressed to . . .

"Hurry up, it's nearly time to take the reading . . ."

The Government's new scheme for Cold Weather payments would mean that pensioners in the West Highlands and Islands would be even less likely than before to receive payments.

This fact emerged following examination of the new order announced by Social Security Minister John Major. The regulations on payments have been revised in the face of long-running protests about their inequity.

There will now be the same "trigger point" throughout the UK of −1.5 degrees centigrade, averaged over a seven-day period. One of the catches is that the seven days will have to run from Monday to Sunday.

But **Free Press** inquiries have shown that readings at Stornoway, the weather station which advises the DHSS for the Western Isles, would *never* have given an average of −1.5 during any week in the past seven years.

This means that pensioners in the Western Isles who were able to claim a Cold Weather payment of £5 per week, during the exceptionally cold spell last winter, would not have been able to do so if the new regulations had been in force! This would have applied to over 90 per cent of Scotland.

28.11.86

"Another British vote of confidence in our system . . ."

Comhairle nan Eilean has turned down a request from the Convention of Scottish Local Authorities that it — in common with other Scottish councils — should make clear its opposition to apartheid and take some token steps in support of that policy . . .

31.10.86

"That's no excuse — you still don't qualify for exemption!"

"Yes, sir, I admit the poll tax only applies to human beings,
but I'm afraid I'm not convinced you are an alien
from the planet Zog!"

22.4.88

20.5.88

Double blow for Staffin as bar closes, minister opposes hall plan

Communities in the Staffin/Kilmuir areas of Skye were dealt a double blow this week with the news that the Flodigarry Hotel was to cease to act as a licensed hotel, while hopes for a village hall at Staffin suffered a set-back following the intervention of the local Free Presbyterian minister . . .

"It's a miracle! The priest's walking on the water!"

WATER-SKIING PRIEST AIMS FOR A RECORD!

In order to help raise money towards the new Eriskay Community Hall, the island's priest Father John Archie MacMillan is asking to be sponsored for water-skiing down the Sound of Eriskay, while simultaneously playing the bagpipes.

"Anything they can do, we can do better . . . !"

12.2.82

18.6.82

"Of course we're not against all the Catholic Church's ideas — we're not bigots, you know!"

Last week Lord MacKay was suspended as an elder of the church and banned from taking communion by the Southern Presbytery of the FP Church, because he attended two Roman Catholic requiem masses.

Autumn 1988

"Honest, your refference, I was only doing the dishes!"

Freemasonry taboo for members of Free Church

30.5.86

"Er . . . Anyone for tennis?"

The Government has rejected calls for a salmon-tagging scheme to be included in its forthcoming legislation promised in last week's Queen's Speech, but it "will provide for the introduction of a salmon dealer licensing scheme in Scotland"

15.11.85

A Lewis reader has come up with a novel way of halting the erosion of the "right" to fish for brown trout in Scotland's rivers and lochs. In a letter to the *Free Press* Mr Norman MacArthur Jr from Carloway suggests that "every available rod could be encouraged to 'Troutaboutabit' on selected waters" next summer. A system could be devised, adds Mr MacArthur, concentrating on waters where harassment from "so-called proprietors" is greatest. For good measure he proposes that points be awarded on a scale of one to 10: fish caught in the most intensely disputed waters carrying a higher value, with those from Grimersta waters at the top of the scale!

29.8.86

"Leave them all locked in until there's only two left standing — they get the job!"

"Nothing in our records, your lairdship!"

The Government have agreed that District Salmon Fishery Boards should have a new power to seek character references from the local police when appointing water bailiffs.

11.3.88

9.5.86

"This lot are more fun than the local poachers!"

"I can't decide whether to make the figures lower to justify
the Salmon Act or higher to show it's working . . ."

THREE LEADING FIGURES in the Garynahine Estate Company were each fined £30 at the same court on Wednesday, on charges of illegal fishing, in a case which brought to the surface local animosities and particularly the feud between Garynahine and neighbouring Grimersta estates.

There has been a call for the Department of Agriculture and Fisheries for Scotland to tighten up their procedures for monitoring salmon catches in the Western Isles.

This follows publication, reported in last week's **Free Press**, of the alleged salmon catches for 1985. The figures showed that — according to returns from proprietors — only 830 salmon were officially caught on Lewis during the year.

In Uist, the catch had apparently jumped from zero in 1984 to 974 in 1985 — more than the official Lewis tally.

25.3.83

2.1.87

"Cheer up, your lairdship — only two days to go!"

Lewis estate's offer of free fishing "patronising"

A Lewis estate's offer of three days' free loch fishing for locals in a bid to discourage "poaching" has been described as "patronising".

Mr Christopher Sheppard, who with a partner has recently taken over Aline Estate, declared last week that free fishing would be available on Loch Langavat on dates in July, August and September, with the added bonus of prizes for the best fish caught.

25.7.86

"Hello, base . . . this undercover agent no 3 . . . Oh, no! They're not poachers, they're wildfowlers!!"

5.2.88

"All we had to do was say the tankers could interfere with the salmon fishing!"

4.7.86

"No, the quarry only supply the earmuffs . . . The glasses are from the manufacturers of Nuvan!"

South Uist Estates are proposing to ban blasting operations at the island's Howmore quarry for seven months of the year on the grounds that the noise will disturb the activities of their fishing tenants.

"Of course we're an endangered species — you've only to look at the dwindling returns!"

As reported last week, the statistics for Scottish salmon catches are again bogus, due to the fact that 103 proprietors simply refused to fill in the forms.

However, the extent to which the statistics are invalid is impossible to judge, without knowing who the errant proprietors are.

[SCENE: the specially fitted toilets in the Gathering Hall at the weekend]

"I say, Roddy old egg. Do hurry up with the jolly old half-bottle."

(The 100th Skye Ball rolled into Portree Gathering Hall at the weekend. The Ball was inaugurated in 1897 by several aristocratic Skye families to provide the west coast upper classes with an annual hooley — although one patron said this week that "just about anybody could get tickets these days, provided they applied in time".)

14.9.79

"I say . . . The officer says someone named Hooray-Henry is illegally parked"

The genteel charm normally associated with the ladies and gentlemen attending the annual Skye Balls was tested to the limit this week as public controversy raged about a decision to grant extra-late licences for the events on Wednesday and Thursday. For while patrons of other less exclusive functions on the island have been ordered to drink up by 1am the guests at the Skye Balls — invites only — were able to whoop it up at the bar in the Skye Gathering Hall until six o'clock in the morning.

"It's OK as long as we stay on this side of the fence, girls!"

27.9.82

Master of all he surveys!

A company based in Northampton is offering Americans the chance to become a "laird" in Wester Ross for $29, through advertisements in the 'Highlander' magazine which circulates among Caledonian Societies and the like.

Prospective "lairds" are asked to send $29 to Highland Enterprises, 1 St Giles Terrace, Northampton. This will give them title to a one square foot plot of land and details of the "exact location" will be forwarded along with a photograph.

The Countess of Sutherland has taken a leaf out of the Duke of Argyll's book and is turning herself into a Trust so that the begging bowl can be thrust in the direction of public funds. She needs, it seems, £70,000 to repair the roof of Dunrobin Castle.

The Department of Environment have already agreed to contribute 25 per cent of the cost and the begging letters are on their way to the HIDB, the Highland Regional Council and the Countryside Commission. The spurious justification for the plea is that Dunrobin serves as a tourist attraction.

20.3.82

Still spreading confusion

Dutch land speculator Johannes Hellinga was back in Skye last week spreading renewed confusion over the land ownership situation in the Waternish area of Skye.

8.10.82

"Hamish and I thought we'd better test the whisky Mr Hellinga gave us . . .!"

Parts of Waternish Estate, bought in 1978 by Mr Johannes Hellinga, have changed hands five time in the course of the past four years, **Free Press** investigations have revealed.

Recently, we disclosed that of the 1,200-acre non-crofting part of the estate, all but 10 acres has now been disposed of by Mr Hellinga. According to solicitors who have been involved in the various dealings, part of the estate has been split up and sold to various Dutch buyers . . .

26.11.82

14.5.82

"When it's spri-ing again, they'll bri-ing again
Landlords from Amsterdam"

23.3.79

"Damn! He's telling the truth! Let him go!"

"It's the Dr John Green Memorial Stone — a sort of farewell gesture"

13.4.79

"Look out! The Kishorn Commandos are back!"

BOOM TIME AGAIN!

25.5.79

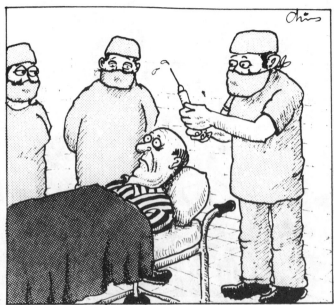

**"So you're a member of Howard Doris management . . .
Hmm, how interesting!"**

The threat by Howard Doris to seek compensation from trade unions over last Wednesday's stoppage at their Kishorn yard this week developed a very hollow ring.

As reported in last week's **Free Press**, the 900 workers at Kishorn voted overwhelmingly to stop work on the trade union day of action in support of the health workers' long-running pay battle . . .

1.10.82

Outbreak of "self-induced illness" hits Kishorn

In a stern lecture by Howard Doris management, workers at the Kishorn platform yard have been warned about the possible consequences of indulging in bouts of "self-induced" illness during working hours . . .

8.7.83

"If whoever threw that lump of jelly doesn't own up at once ..."

Kishorn workers go back

The Kishorn oil platform yard in Wester Ross was back at work as we went to press following a brief stoppage by about 500 workers after a number of their colleagues were suspended — apparently for throwing jelly at each other in the site canteen!

The nine men were suspended on Saturday after the company alleged they had "misbehaved" in the canteen. This was regarded by management as grounds for suspension, although one shop steward accused management of adopting a "Dickensian" attitude in their relationship with the workforce.

The workers came out on strike because they considered their colleagues had been dismissed.

"Just leave your souls with the personnel manager, and we'll get right on to the medical ..."

On Wednesday night, as we went to press, a union official said there was "a distinct possibility" that at least some of the 500 sacked Kishorn workers would get their jobs back . . .

20.3.81

24.4.81

"That's the Kishorn Memorial Paper Mountain — made of the consultancy reports of the Howard Doris Trust . . ."

Almost half the funds distributed by the Howard Doris Trust since the end of 1986 have been used up in consultancy fees and feasibility studies by AMARC — the company appointed by the trustees to investigate how the trust could best be used to benefit Lochcarron and South-West Ross following the closure of the Kishorn yard . . .

"Hello . . .
Is that the minister's wife . . .?"

The dismissal of seven Kishorn workers for behaviour "offensive to the community" during off-duty time is to be fought by their union, the TGWU, and by the workers themselves.

The girls who were employed by Gardner Merchant, the catering firm, were sacked on the spot following a late-night visit two days ago, from a group of male employees . . .

. . . Across the road from the house is the Free Presbyterian manse and the workers believe that the minister, seeing this little flurry of activity, telephoned to Kishorn and made a complaint. Security guards arrived at the house a short time after . . .

The Kishorn Memorial Swimming Pool?

"Another case of frostbite from the naturist beach, doctor."

(This week, Comhairle nan Eilean were to discuss a request by the Central Council for british Naturism that beaches in the Western Isles should be designated for naked bathing. Council officials felt that the climate in the islands militated against such a proposal.)

9.2.79

"False alarm, girls, it's just another local!"

9.4.82

"There you are, girls, I told you he was a pervert!"

DAFS rams "not up to the job"!

DAFS have asked crofters who are dissatisfied with the fertility of rams hired from the Department to report them to Inverness.

19.10.84

A number of items of general interest to crofters and farmers in the islands appear in the latest issue of the North of Scotland College of Agriculture's 'Crofters' Newsletter' for Lewis and Harris.

The newsletter reports that a number of crofters in the islands are to try housing their ewes this winter in an attempt at more efficient husbandry.

28.8.81

"I say, my good man, what odds are you offering on Point Players to win the drama festival?"

The proposed new cultural centre for Stornoway would be devalued by the presence next door of a betting shop, a public inquiry was told this week.

22.1.82

Applecross jam factory plan turns sour

A commercial jam-making experiment on Applecross Estate has been set back following objections from the environmental health department in Dingwall.

One of the department's main concerns was that the lead content in the water supply to the jam-making "factory" was too high, but this week the depute director of environmental health, Mr George Lemmon, gave an assurance that the supply in question is not the one which feeds the Applecross village.

19.2.82

"Come along, Algernon: It sounds as if they've started already!"

Three Stornoway hotels were this week granted permission to open their doors for afternoon drinking from April until October — but only by the casting vote of Western Isles Licensing Board chairman Mr James MacRae.

He said that by granting the extensions there would be greater control of such drinking, instead of people taking their carry-outs to "one of the opera houses". Our Lewis readers will readily understand the reference — the public toilets used for afternoon drinking are known locally as "opera houses" because of the Gaelic singing which normally accompanies such tippling!

29.9.86

Tourists visiting Lewis this season are going to find accommodation in the main centre of Stornoway very difficult to come by because of the number of outside workers employed at the Arnish oil fabrication yard.

"Who's been drinking MY beer? Bloody Goldilocks?"

HERCULES UNCHAINED!

Hercules, the bear which went missing on the east coast of Benbecula while on location filming a TV commercial last Thursday, had still not been spotted as we went to press on Wednesday.

4.4.80

29.80.80

"What a coincidence! Isn't that the officer who arrested you for poaching?"

21.8.81

"Better ring the United Nations — looks like there's been another border incident up at Pictland..."

"Robbie the Pict" comes home

An acre of heather and grassland at Tote is the "promised land" for a gentleman rejoicing in the name of Robbie the Pict!

Mr Pict — alias Brian Robertson — renounced his British citizenship over eight years ago to become "a Pictish national". The gift of land to form the headquarters of Robbie's Pictish Free State has come from Skye & Lochalsh district councillor Mr Donald Cameron. It is understood that the only piece of paper to exchange hands so far is a "promissory note" — the title deeds are apparently in the process of being transferred.

The land, said Robbie, is to be "declared independent" and free from all interference by the English Crown. He described it as "Pict Land of Alba".

Mr Cameron said he had met Robbie several years ago and "found him to be an intriguing character". He added: "We have met on few occasions since then and in a joke I offered Robbie a plot of my land, and he took me up on this."

The uncrowned king of the Pict Land of Alba was due to visit Skye this week. He described the Pictish Free State as "a spiritual and mental alliance of a Celtic tribe" and as "a state of mind".

19.9.86

A policeman based at Portree is convinced he has seen a "ghost" car in Skye, on a stretch of moor road which featured two decades ago in the national press for the same reason . . .

27.4.79

"I see, constable. But how do you know it was a ghost car?"

WAS IT A BIRD, WAS IT A PLANE . . .?

Reports of UFO sightings over Skye at the weekend were confirmed on Monday by police at Portree . . .

A typical Mod ceilidh in the eyes of some beholders . . .

21.3.80

19.10.79

"Obviously that *wasn't* a holiday cottage!"

Gaelic language activists this week denied that they had anything to do with inscribing the word "saorsa" in large letters on five holiday homes in the Braes area of Skye . . .

"Aye, Aye. Another lemonade factory, I presume?"

Slàinte to lemonade!

The lemonade factory in Staffin was back in production this week . . .

Skye man's £5,500 phone bill

A Skye man has been told by British Telecom that if he wants a telephone installed in his home at Rigg, on the main Portree-Staffin road, it will cost him a whacking £5,484!

Clam diver Dave Patfield said he first applied to have a phone put in about seven years ago, when he was quoted a price of £500 — a fairly hefty sum at the time. A few years later, when he again inquired, the cost had jumped to £4,000 . . .

"In the end it proved cheaper to build our own satellite ground station . . ."

1988

"From the Chief Coastguard: 'Apologies for mis-print . . . should have said discontinue use of breeches buoy'!"

Coastguards on the west coast have reacted furiously to the announcement by Paul Channon, Minister for Transport, that breeches buoy gear and line-throwing equipment is to be withdrawn from coastal stations thoughout Britain.

24.8.84

Once again, the Mallaig-Armadale ferry has been suddenly reduced to a passenger-only service — to the annoyance of Sleat hoteliers . . .

26.2.88

"This joker must be getting good fishing — according to his reported position he's on the M6 south of Birmingham . . .

The Coastguard at Oban have started a fishing boat reporting system — "Oban Line" — to improve safety and response times to any off-shore emergencies. The system already operates successfully in the North Sea where boats report their position at 12-hourly intervals by way of a standard grid or a grid unique to the boat.

"Funny how the rabbits seem bigger since Chernobyl . . ."

The owner of the valued Portree beauty-spot of Ben Chrachaig said this week that he was "hopeful" of reaching agreement with the Australian branch of the Clan MacNicol Society who are negotiating to buy the 140-acre site . . .

5.12.86

3.10.86

"Consider your car well and truly launched!"

TOYOTA TAKE THE ROAD TO THE ISLES

A total of some 160 motoring journalists from all over Britain are expected to descend on Skye in October for the launch of a new car.

The event has been organised by Toyota (GB) Ltd to present a new model to the press. During the week 4th-8th October they have invited 160 journalists to come to Skye to try it out and, in the words of the Toyota press release, "to sample the delights of your island"...

13.8.82

Eachann getting into the spirit of the Mod

23.10.82

Yet another advertising film is being made this week in Skye, but one with a difference because it is promoting a local product — Talisker whisky. On Thursday the thatched cottages at Luib were to be the setting for an 1860s costume re-enactment of a scene from the clearances complete with local acting talent, and the Old Inn at Carbost will feature in the ceilidh scene.

"OK, skipper — we've found a way of loading without using the foreshore . . ."

A major order which is in prospect for Alltanavaig quarry in Skye is in danger of being lost because of protracted negotiations over foreshore rights, according to information received by the **Free Press** . . .

"I told you the sea defences needed strengthened!"

EROSION THREAT TO SOUTH UIST COAST

"Actually, brother, when we instructed you to 'black' the pool . . ."

The union NALGO has "blacked" the vacant managerial post at Portree Swimming Pool, which has been closed since mid-December following the dismissal of the pool manager . . .

"Aye, we picked up a few ideas on the tour!"

The Harris Tweed Association are off to Japan in May as part of their biggest-ever promotional exercise . . .

7.2.86

"It's like shooting fish in a barrel!"

The latest proposals by Strath-aird Farms Ltd for expanding their fish farming operations in Skye involve the siting of cages for smolt rearing in Loch Leathan, on the road between Portree and Staffin . . .

. . . Portree Angling Association, who have the fishing rights to the loch, say they have no objections to the proposals.

PLAYING FIELD
KEEP OUT
by order
Chris

"How did the old overgrown wood get its name? Well, long, long ago there were two feuding clans, the McShinties and the MacSoccers . . ."

An attempt is likely to be made to overturn a decision taken this week to ban the use of the King George V playing field at Portree for a period of two years . . .

. . . Chief executive David Noble said on Wednesday: "A six-month rest would get the shinty pitch into a fairly adequate condition, given a good spell, but the football pitch would have to have a longer rest . . .

30.1.87

Princely sum offered for spuds

The latest media spin-off to emerge from Prince Charles' much publicised visit to Berneray earlier in the year is the "potato auction" story that padded the pages of many national papers this week.

Apparently top hotels in Britain had approached the residents of Berneray to buy the very potatoes that the Prince planted during his stay on the island and were willing top pay up to £10 per pound for the royal spuds. However, the people of Berneray refused to become souvenir mercenaries and spurned all approaches.

How the hotels could have identified the potatoes as "Charlies" had the crofters accepted the offer did not merit feature-length debate in the press and must remain a source of intrigue to many readers.

Treading water for charity

A sponsored event to rival the water ski-ing bagpipe-playing priest of Barra is to be undertaken next Tuesday when Portree man Drew Millar plans to run across the Minch from Uig to Tarbert in order to raise money for polio research!

Being a butcher to trade Mr Millar is not receiving any divine assistance in his attempt to run on water, but Cal-Mac are stepping in with a complimentary ferry trip to help him out.

In fact, if the truth be told, Mr Millar will not even get his trainers damp crossing the Minch as he will be running on an electric treadmill aboard the MV 'Iona' while she makes her scheduled trip from Skye to Harris.

Because of the international status of Harris Tweed among the world's leading fashion fabrics, Stornoway has been chosen by the organisers of Premier Vision of Paris — the twice-yearly fabric trade fair — as the first UK venue for their annual general meeting which is held in a different textile venue each year . . .

5.6.87

"I know your satellite navigation systems says we're at Sligachan, but this gentleman says it's 35 miles that way . . ."

A group of eminent scientists were due to arrive in Skye at the weekend for a three-day visit combining business with pleasure.

They are members of the governing council of the International Society for Photogrammetry and Remote Sensing. They were gathered this week — together with 300 scientists from around the world — for a symposium in Edinburgh and decided they should see the other side of Scotland before returning to their respective countries.

Photogrammetry is the science of mapping objects from stereo photography; remote sensing involves the use of electronic scanners (usually in satellites) to provide information in natural resources, vegetation and geology.

12.9.86

"Oh no! Not YOU again!"